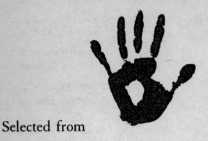

Selected from

Love Medicine

Louise Erdrich

Supplementary material by the staff of
Literacy Volunteers of New York City

Writers' Voices
Literacy Volunteers of New York City

LITERACY VOLUNTEERS OF NEW YORK CITY INC.

Selected from

Love Medicine

Louise Erdrich

WRITERS' VOICES® was made possible by grants from
The Booth Ferris Foundation, The Vincent Astor Foundation,
and The Scripps-Howard Foundation.

.   .   .

ATTENTION READERS: We would like to hear what you
think about our books. Please send your comments or
suggestions to:

> The Editors
> Literacy Volunteers of New York City
> 666 Broadway, #520
> New York, NY 10012

.   .   .

Printed in The United States of America

96 95 94 93 92 91 90   10 9 8 7 6 5 4 3 2 1

First LVNYC Printing: January 1989

ISBN 0-929631-02-1

Writers' Voices is a series of books published by Literacy
Volunteers of New York City Inc., 666 Broadway, New
York, NY 10012. The words, "Writers' Voices," are a
trademark of Literacy Volunteers of New York City.
Designed by Paul Davis Studio

Acknowledgments

Literacy Volunteers of New York City gratefully acknowledges the generous support of the following foundations which made the publication of WRITERS' VOICES and NEW WRITERS' VOICES possible: The Booth Ferris Foundation, The Vincent Astor Foundation, and The Scripps-Howard Foundation. We also wish to thank Hildy Simmons, Linda L. Gillies, and David Hendin for their assistance.

This book could not have been realized without the kind and generous cooperation of the author, Louise Erdrich, and her publisher, Henry Holt and Company, Inc. We are also grateful to Michael Dorris for his encouragement and support. Molly Braun was most helpful in our picture search.

We deeply appreciate the contributions of the following suppliers: Cam Steel Rule Die Works, Inc. (steel cutting die for display); Domtar Industries Inc. (text stock); Federal Paper Board Company, Inc. and Milton Paper Company Inc. (cover stock); Jackson Typesetting (text typesetting); Lancer Graphic Industries Inc. (cover printing); Martin/Friess Communications (display header); Mergenthaler Container (corrugated display); Offset Paperback Mfrs., Inc., A Bertelsmann Company (text printing and binding); and Stevenson Photo Color Company (cover color separations).

For their guidance and assistance, we wish to thank the *Writers' Voices* Advisory Committee: committee chair James E. Galton, Marvel Comics; Jeff Brown; George P. Davidson, Ballantine Books; Susan Kaminsky; Parker B. Ladd, Association of American

Publishers; Jerry Sirchia, Association of American Publishers; Benita Somerfield; and Irene Yuss, New American Library.

In the planning stages of this series, the following volunteer tutors and staff members were most helpful in testing the concepts: Betty Ballard, Louisa Brooke, Dan Cohen, Marilyn Collins, Ann Keniston, Elizabeth Mann, Gary Murphy, Isabel Steinberg, and June Wilkins.

For generously giving of their time and expertise, we want to thank F. Robert Stein (legal advice); Gene Durante (operations advice); Jacque Cook, Sharon Darling, Donald Graves, Doris Gunderson, Renée Lerche, and Dorothy Strickland (peer reviewers); and Pat Fogarty, Kathleen Gray, and Ingrid Strauch (copyediting and proofreading).

Our thanks to Paul Davis Studio and Claudia Bruno, José Conde, Myrna Davis, Paul Davis, and Jeanine Esposito for the inspired design of the books and their covers. We would also like to thank Barbara A. Mancuso of *The New York Times* Pictures for her help with photo research and selection.

For their marketing assistance and support, our thanks to the Mass Market Education Committee of the Association of American Publishers. For her publicity skills, we thank Barbara J. Hendra of Barbara Hendra Associates.

LVNYC staff members Gary Murphy and Sarah Wilkinson made numerous helpful suggestions. And finally, special credit must be given to Marilyn Boutwell and Jean Fargo of the LVNYC staff for their major contributions to the educational and editorial content of these books.

Contents

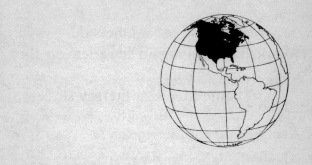

·····Route of Henry and Lyman's trip

About *Writers' Voices*

"I want to read what others do—what I see people reading in libraries, on the subway, and at home."

Mamie Moore, a literacy student,
Brooklyn, New York

Writers' Voices is our response to Mamie Moore's wish:

the wish to step forward into the reading community,
the wish to have access to new information,
the wish to read to her grandchildren,
the wish to read for the joy of reading.

Note to the Reader

"What we are familiar with, we cease to see. The writer shakes up the familiar scene, and as if by magic, we see a new meaning in it."

Anaïs Nin

Writers' Voices invites you to discover new meaning. One way to discover new meaning is to learn something new. Another is to see in a new way something you already know. Writers touch us by writing about familiar things—love, family, death, for example. Even if the experiences in a book are different from our own, the emotions may be familiar. Our own thoughts and feelings let us interact with the author's story.

Writers' Voices is a series of books. Each book contains unedited selections from one writer's work. We chose the selections because the writers' voices can be clearly heard. Also, they deal with experiences that are interesting to think about and discuss.

If you are a new reader, you may want to have a selection read aloud to you, perhaps more than once. This will free you to enjoy the piece, to hear the language used, and to think about its meaning. Even if you are a more experienced reader, you may enjoy hearing the selection read aloud before reading it silently to yourself.

Each selection is set in a framework to expand your understanding of the selection. The framework includes a chapter that tells about the writer's life. Some authors write about their own lives; other authors write stories from their imagination. You may wonder why an author chose to write what he or she did. Sometimes you can find the answer by knowing about the author's life.

You may also find chapters about the characters, the plot, and when or where the story took place. These will help you begin thinking about the selection. They will also help you understand what may be unfamiliar to you.

We believe that to be a reader, you must be at the center of the reading process. We believe you learn best when you choose what you will read. We encourage you to read *actively*. An active reader does many things—while reading, and before and after reading—that help him or her better understand and enjoy a book. Here are some suggestions of things you can do:

Before Reading
- Read the front and back covers of the book, and look at the cover illustration. Think about what you expect the book to be about, based on this information.
- Think about why you want to read this book.
- Ask yourself what you want to discover, and what questions you hope will be answered.
- Think about how your own experiences and knowledge can help you better understand the book.

During Reading

- Try to stay with the rhythm of the language. If you find any words or sentences you don't understand, keep reading to see if the meaning becomes clear. If it doesn't, go back and reread the difficult part or discuss it with others. If you prefer to wait until you have read the whole story before you reread the difficult part, underline it so it will be easy to find later.

- Put yourself into the story. If you feel left out, ask why. Is it the writing? Is it something else?

- Ask yourself questions as you read. For example: Do I believe this story or this character? Why?

After Reading

- Ask yourself if the story makes you see any of your own experiences in a new way.

- Ask yourself if the story has given you any new information.

- Keep a journal in which you can

write down your thoughts about what you have read, and save new words you have learned.

• Discuss what you have read with others.

Good writing should make you think after you put the book down. Whether you are a beginning reader, a more experienced reader, or a teacher of reading, we encourage you to take time to think about these books and to discuss your thoughts with others.

When you finish a selection, you may want to choose among the questions and suggested activities that follow. They are meant to help you discover more about what you have read and how it relates to you—as a person, as a reader, and as a writer.

When you are finished with the book, we hope you will write to our editors about your reactions. We want to know your thoughts about our books, and what they have meant to you.

About Louise Erdrich

Louise Erdrich was born in Little Falls, Minnesota, on July 6, 1954. She grew up in North Dakota and is a tribal member of the Turtle Mountain Band of Chippewas.

Contemporary Authors quotes Louise Erdrich: "My father used to give me a nickel for every story I wrote, and my mother wove strips of construction paper together and stapled them into book covers. . . .Mine were wonderful parents; they got me excited about reading and writing in a lasting way."

She went to school at the Wahpeton Indian Boarding School and then to Dartmouth College. She has a master's degree from The Johns Hopkins University. She won the National Book Critics Circle Award for *Love Medicine*, her first novel.

Louise Erdrich lives in New Hampshire with her husband, Michael Dorris, who is a teacher and writer. They have five children.

About Native Americans

This chapter provides a short historical background for the selection.

The first people to migrate to America came from Asia thousands of years ago. They were here long before the people who came from Europe, living in all parts of what is now the United States. They had many different tribes and cultures. They are the true native Americans.

The first Europeans to land in North America were trying to get to India. When they reached this country, they thought they had found it. So they called the native Americans "Indians."

Native Americans believed that all things in the universe had spirit and life. People needed to find harmony within themselves and with everything in the universe. Religion was a part of everyday life, and inspired all their activities.

They had many myths, stories, songs,

and dances that expressed their beliefs. Storytelling was an important part of life, used to teach as well as to keep traditions alive.

Tribes were governed by councils, not by one person. Decisions were made according to custom and tradition, and older people were greatly respected on the councils. Wisdom, and an understanding of the tribe's history, were among the most important qualities a person could have.

Tribes lived by hunting wild animals, and by fishing, farming, and gathering wild plants. Many of these wild plants were moved into gardens, and became important crops, such as corn, tomatoes, and beans.

To feed and clothe its people, each tribe needed a great deal of land. And though each tribe might have its own general territory, tribes often shared the same hunting grounds. Native Americans believed that the land could never belong to one person. The Omaha tribe said, "The earth is like fire and water that cannot be sold."

When Europeans came to America, life was changed for the Native Americans. The Europeans had different attitudes toward the land. They believed that land should belong to individuals who could use it to benefit their own families. They used the natural resources of the land for such businesses as fur trading and lumbering. And as more and more Europeans came to America, they wanted more and more land.

The Native Americans, under such leaders as Sitting Bull, Crazy Horse, and Geronimo, fought many wars with the European settlers over their land. The wars began in the 1600s and continued for more than two hundred years in different parts of the country. In these wars, the Native Americans were almost always defeated, and had to sign agreements about what land they would give up.

As the Native Americans gave up more

and more land, they were pushed into smaller and smaller areas. Sometimes the government forced them completely out of the area in which they had always lived.

The Native Americans saw their land as the source of life. They believed that land was a living thing. They adapted to the land; they did not force the land to adapt to them. The culture of each tribe was based on the kind of land on which it lived—in mountains or on the plains, by lakes or in the desert. When the land was lost, precious parts of Native American culture were destroyed.

In 1830, the United States government created an Indian Territory in the West. Eastern tribes were forced to move there. Later, the government chose areas of land in various states for particular tribes. These were called reservations.

The Native Americans opposed the government's deciding where they should live, and they also were saddened by the changes in their lives and culture. In

1879, Chief Joseph of the Nez Perce tribe said, "Let me be a free man—free to travel, free to stop, free to work, free to trade where I choose, free to choose my own teachers, free to follow the religion of my fathers, free to think and talk and act for myself."

It was not until the 1930s and 1940s that laws were passed to support the traditions and land claims of Native Americans. But this did not last long. In the 1950s, the government again passed laws that were hurtful to Native American tribes.

In the 1960s and 1970s, Native Americans became more active in the effort to change things. They tried to work together to improve their condition, and to make the government honor the agreements it had made with them.

Congress has guaranteed for many tribes the protection of their lands and the right to their own government. Tribes so protected by the Congress make many of their own laws, usually through a tribal council.

Not all tribes live on federally-protected reservations. Some live on other kinds of reservations, others in communities of their own. And many individuals live in cities across the country.

There are Native Americans in every state. California has the most, about 200,000. The state with the least is Vermont, with about 1,000.

Native Americans are still striving to better their lot. On the reservations today, many suffer from poverty and a lack of education and health care. But, as these Native Americans have gained more control over their lives, they have also regained their pride and their identity.

About the Vietnam War

This chapter provides a short historical background for the selection.

Vietnam is in Southeast Asia, a small, semi-tropical country covered by jungles and rice fields.

Vietnam has been ruled by foreign countries for much of its history. Most recently, it was under France's rule. The Vietnamese people fought for independence and defeated the French.

In 1954, a treaty was signed that ended the war with France. Until the Vietnamese people could hold elections to decide who would lead their country, Vietnam was divided into two parts. The northern part was governed by Communists. The Communists wanted Vietnam to be one country, under their rule. The southern part was governed by Premier Diem, a leader opposed to the Communists and friendly to the United States.

Many South Vietnamese were poor

farmers who lived in small villages. They
had fought beside the Communists during
the war. Now they became angry with
the government of South Vietnam because it refused to hold elections, and
because of the rent it made them pay for
their land.

These peasants were joined by men
from North Vietnam in the fight against
the South Vietnamese government. In
the late 1950s, the United States began
sending money and political consultants
to South Vietnam. In the early 1960s, it
began sending military advisers to help
the government of South Vietnam de-
feat the guerrilla forces. Then it began
sending troops.

When American armed forces first
went there, almost no Americans had ever
heard of Vietnam, or knew where it
was. But the war turned out to be the
longest in the history of the United States.
It lasted until 1975.

Three million American men and
women served in Vietnam. More than

57,000 were killed, and 300,000 were wounded. Hundreds of thousands of Vietnamese people were killed—women, children, and old people, as well as soldiers.

The war in Vietnam was fought mostly in the jungle. This terrain, with its many rivers and small villages, made it hard to know where the enemy was hiding. Often the enemy knew the countryside, and was supported by the local villagers. American soldiers were never sure who was a friend, who was an enemy.

In the dense jungle, it was easy for a squad to get separated from its platoon. Fighting could break out anywhere. Booby traps and land mines were everywhere.

More bombs were dropped on Vietnam during this war than in all the wars in the world before it. A chemical weapon called Agent Orange was used to destroy the leaves of jungle trees and plants that hid the enemy. It was later discovered that this chemical caused health problems for the people and animals who came in contact with it.

At the beginning of the war, most people in the United States believed it was important to help South Vietnam. As the war went on, however, many Americans began to change their minds.

All over the United States, people began to protest the war. Some people felt that the Vietnamese should be left alone to solve their problems. Others were opposed to the weapons being used, and to the fact that so many civilians were being killed. Still others thought we could spend our money far better at home than in Vietnam.

Many Americans, however, continued to support the war. They wanted to help keep South Vietnam a separate, non-communist country. They thought it would be wrong to abandon the South Vietnamese. And they believed that too many lives had been lost and too much money had been spent for the United States just to give up.

As the war went on, and more and more American soldiers were killed, the opposition grew. Thousands and thousands of people marched in protests against the war. Some young men refused to be drafted. There were demonstrations at colleges during which protestors were killed.

The American troops in Vietnam were confused. For many, the war did not make sense, and they did not want to die for a cause they did not understand. Many of them thought the war could never be won. Many felt betrayed by the protestors at home, felt that their protests cast shame on every person who had died for his country in Vietnam.

American troops began to return from Vietnam in the early 1970s. In the United States, they were not treated like heroes or helped by the generous programs for veterans that had been offered after other wars.

Bernard Edelman, in his book, *Dear America: Letters Home From Vietnam*, says:

"Most veterans felt scorned. Perhaps worse, they felt ignored by all but their families after one of the most intense experiences of their lives. In the jungle one day, they were back home 48 hours later. Little had changed since they'd been gone—except them.... There was no period of national mourning for those who died, no outpouring of thanks for those who returned, no welcoming embrace by a grateful nation. Some were ashamed of their service and wouldn't, or couldn't, talk about it."

The veterans of the Vietnam War, both men and women, had trouble getting jobs. Many had health problems. Some had been affected by chemicals used in the war. Others had become addicted to drugs while in Vietnam. Some had psychological problems because of the terrible experiences they had been through.

Vietnam veterans organized to demand support, and have gotten help for many of those who have needed it. Most Vietnam veterans have been able to build new lives.

America was torn by this war. One of the acts that helped heal the wounds was the building of the Vietnam Veterans Memorial in Washington, D.C. On the memorial are the names of all those who died in Vietnam.

Today, Vietnam is one country, governed by the Communists.

The Vietnam Veterans Memorial in Washington, D.C. (Credit: George Tames/*The New York Times*)

About the Selection from
Love Medicine

Love Medicine is about two Native American families, the Kashpaws and the Lamartines. *The Red Convertible* is one of the stories in the book; it is about the Lamartines.

The Lamartine family lives on a reservation in North Dakota. They belong to the Chippewa (or Ojibway) tribe. This tribe lives in the Great Plains (the midwestern United States and Canada).

The story of *The Red Convertible* is told by Lyman Lamartine. He tells about his older brother, Henry Junior, and their red convertible.

Lyman and his brother buy the convertible in 1970 and take a long trip in it that summer. When they return, Henry is called into the marines to fight in Vietnam. When he comes home over three years later, he is a changed person. Lyman thinks the red convertible might help his brother become more like his old self.

Perhaps this story will make you think about a difficult time you experienced and how your friends and family helped you through it. Or perhaps it will make you think about a special possession and what it meant to you.

Selected from

Love Medicine

The Red Convertible

(1974)

LYMAN LAMARTINE

I was the first one to drive a convertible
on my reservation. And of course it was
red, a red Olds. I owned that car along
with my brother Henry Junior. We
owned it together until his boots filled
with water on a windy night and he
bought out my share. Now Henry owns
the whole car, and his younger brother
Lyman (that's myself), Lyman walks
everywhere he goes.

How did I earn enough money to buy

my share in the first place? My one
talent was I could always make money.
I had a touch for it, unusual in a Chippewa. From the first I was different that
way, and everyone recognized it. I was
the only kid they let in the American
Legion Hall to shine shoes, for example,
and one Christmas I sold spiritual bou-
quets for the mission door to door. The
nuns let me keep a percentage. Once I
started, it seemed the more money I
made the easier the money came. Everyone encouraged it. When I was fifteen I
got a job washing dishes at the Joliet
Café, and that was where my first big
break happened.

It wasn't long before I was promoted
to bussing tables, and then the short-
order cook quit and I was hired to take
her place. No sooner than you know it I
was managing the Joliet. The rest is
history. I went on managing. I soon
became part owner, and of course there
was no stopping me then. It wasn't long
before the whole thing was mine.

After I'd owned the Joliet for one year, it blew over in the worst tornado ever seen around here. The whole operation was smashed to bits. A total loss. The fryalator was up in a tree, the grill torn in half like it was paper. I was only sixteen. I had it all in my mother's name, and I lost it quick, but before I lost it I had every one of my relatives, and their relatives, to dinner, and I also bought that red Olds I mentioned, along with Henry.

The first time we saw it! I'll tell you when we first saw it. We had gotten a ride up to Winnipeg, and both of us had money. Don't ask me why, because we never mentioned a car or anything, we just had all our money. Mine was cash, a big bankroll from the Joliet's insurance. Henry had two checks—a week's extra pay for being laid off, and his regular check from the Jewel Bearing Plant.

We were walking down Portage anyway, seeing the sights, when we saw it.

There it was, parked, large as life. Really as *if* it was alive. I thought of the word *repose,* because the car wasn't simply stopped, parked, or whatever. That car reposed, calm and gleaming, a FOR SALE sign in its left front window. Then, before we had thought it over at all, the car belonged to us and our pockets were empty. We had just enough money for gas back home.

We went places in that car, me and Henry. We took off driving all one whole summer. We started off toward the Little Knife River and Mandaree in Fort Berthold and then we found ourselves down in Wakpala somehow, and then suddenly we were over in Montana on the Rocky Boys, and yet the summer was not even half over. Some people hang on to details when they travel, but we didn't let them bother us and just lived our everyday lives here to there.

I do remember this one place with willows. I remember I laid under those trees and it was comfortable. So comfortable. The branches bent down all around me like a tent or a stable. And quiet, it was quiet, even though there was a powwow close enough so I could see it going on. The air was not too still, not too windy either. When the dust rises up and hangs in the air around the dancers like that, I feel good. Henry was asleep with his arms thrown wide. Later on, he woke up and we started driving again. We were somewhere in Montana, or maybe on the Blood Reserve—it could have been anywhere. Anyway it was where we met the girl.

All her hair was in buns around her ears, that's the first thing I noticed about her. She was posed alongside the road with her arm out, so we stopped. That girl was short, so short her lumber shirt looked comical on her, like a nightgown. She had jeans on and fancy moccasins and she carried a little suitcase.

"Hop on in," says Henry. So she climbs in between us.

"We'll take you home," I says. "Where do you live?"

"Chicken," she says.

"Where the hell's that?" I ask her.

"Alaska."

"Okay," says Henry, and we drive. We got up there and never wanted to leave. The sun doesn't truly set there in summer, and the night is more a soft dusk. You might doze off, sometimes, but before you know it you're up again, like an animal in nature. You never feel like you have to sleep hard or put away the world. And things would grow up there. One day just dirt or moss, the next day flowers and long grass. The girl's name was Susy. Her family really took to us. They fed us and put us up. We had our own tent to live in by their house, and the kids would be in and out of there all day and night. They couldn't get over me and Henry being brothers, we looked so different. We told them we knew we had the same mother, anyway.

One night Susy came in to visit us.

We sat around in the tent talking of this thing and that. The season was changing. It was getting darker by that time, and the cold was even getting just a little mean. I told her it was time for us to go. She stood up on a chair.

"You never seen my hair," Susy said.

That was true. She was standing on a chair, but still, when she unclipped her buns the hair reached all the way to the ground. Our eyes opened. You couldn't tell how much hair she had when it was rolled up so neatly. Then my brother Henry did something funny. He went up to the chair and said, "Jump on my shoulders." So she did that, and her hair reached down past his waist, and he started twirling, this way and that, so her hair was flung out from side to side.

"I always wondered what it was like to have long pretty hair," Henry says. Well we laughed. It was a funny sight, the way he did it. The next morning we got up and took leave of those people.

• • •

On to greener pastures, as they say. It was down through Spokane and across Idaho then Montana and very soon we were racing the weather right along under the Canadian border through Columbus, Des Lacs, and then we were in Bottineau County and soon home. We'd made most of the trip, that summer, without putting up the car hood at all. We got home just in time, it turned out, for the army to remember Henry had signed up to join it.

I don't wonder that the army was so glad to get my brother that they turned him into a Marine. He was built like a brick outhouse anyway. We liked to tease him that they really wanted him for his Indian nose. He had a nose big and sharp as a hatchet, like the nose on Red Tomahawk, the Indian who killed Sitting Bull, whose profile is on signs all along the North Dakota highways. Henry went off to training camp, came home once during Christmas, then the next thing you know we got an overseas letter from him. It was 1970, and he said he was stationed up in the northern hill country. Whereabouts I did not know. He wasn't such a hot letter writer, and only got off two before the enemy caught him. I could never keep it straight, which direction those good Vietnam soldiers were from.

I wrote him back several times, even though I didn't know if those letters would get through. I kept him informed all about the car. Most of the time I had it up on blocks in the yard or half taken apart, because that long trip did a hard job on it under the hood.

I always had good luck with numbers, and never worried about the draft myself. I never even had to think about what my number was. But Henry was never lucky in the same way as me. It was at least three years before Henry came home. By then I guess the whole war was solved in the government's mind, but for him it would keep on going. In those years I'd put his car into almost perfect shape. I always thought of it as his car while he was gone, even though when he left he said, "Now it's yours," and threw me his key.

"Thanks for the extra key," I'd said. "I'll put it up in your drawer just in case I need it." He laughed.

When he came home, though, Henry was very different, and I'll say this: the change was no good. You could hardly expect him to change for the better, I know. But he was quiet, so quiet, and never comfortable sitting still anywhere but always up and moving around. I thought back to times we'd sat still for whole afternoons, never moving a muscle, just shifting our weight along the ground, talking to whoever sat with us, watching things. He'd always had a joke, then, too, and now you couldn't get him to laugh, or when he did it was more the sound of a man choking, a sound that stopped up the throats of other people around him. They got to leaving him alone most of the time, and I didn't blame them. It was a fact: Henry was jumpy and mean.

I'd bought a color TV set for my mom and the rest of us while Henry was away. Money still came very easy. I was sorry I'd ever bought it though, because of Henry. I was also sorry I'd bought color, because with black-and-white the pictures seem older and farther away. But what are you going to do? He sat in front of it, watching it, and that was the only time he was completely still. But it was the kind of stillness that you see in a rabbit when it freezes and before it will bolt. He was not easy. He sat in his chair gripping the armrests with all his might, as if the chair itself was moving at a high speed and if he let go at all he would rocket forward and maybe crash right through the set.

Once I was in the room watching TV with Henry and I heard his teeth click

at something. I looked over, and he'd
bitten through his lip. Blood was going
down his chin. I tell you right then I
wanted to smash that tube to pieces. I
went over to it but Henry must have
known what I was up to. He rushed
from his chair and shoved me out of the
way, against the wall. I told myself he
didn't know what he was doing.

My mom came in, turned the set off
real quiet, and told us she had made
something for supper. So we went and
sat down. There was still blood going
down Henry's chin, but he didn't notice
it and no one said anything, even though
every time he took a bite of his bread
his blood fell onto it until he was eating
his own blood mixed in with the food.

While Henry was not around we talked
about what was going to happen to him.
There were no Indian doctors on the
reservation, and my mom was afraid of
trusting Old Man Pillager because he
courted her long ago and was jealous of

her husbands. He might take revenge through her son. We were afraid that if we brought Henry to a regular hospital they would keep him.

"They don't fix them in those places," Mom said; "they just give them drugs."

"We wouldn't get him there in the first place," I agreed, "so let's just forget about it."

Then I thought about the car.

Henry had not even looked at the car since he'd gotten home, though like I said, it was in tip-top condition and ready to drive. I thought the car might bring the old Henry back somehow. So I bided my time and waited for my chance to interest him in the vehicle.

One night Henry was off somewhere. I took myself a hammer. I went out to that car and I did a number on its underside. Whacked it up. Bent the tail pipe double. Ripped the muffler loose. By the time I was done with the car it looked worse than any typical Indian car that has been driven all its life on reser-

vation roads, which they always say are
like government promises—full of holes.
It just about hurt me, I'll tell you that! I
threw dirt in the carburetor and I ripped
all the electric tape off the seats. I made
it look just as beat up as I could. Then I
sat back and waited for Henry to find it.

Still, it took him over a month. That
was all right, because it was just getting
warm enough, not melting, but warm
enough to work outside.

"Lyman," he says, walking in one day,
"that red car looks like shit."

"Well it's old," I says. "You got to
expect that."

"No way!" says Henry. "That car's a
classic! But you went and ran the piss
right out of it, Lyman, and you know it
don't deserve that. I kept that car in
A-one shape. You don't remember. You're
too young. But when I left, that car was
running like a watch. Now I don't even
know if I can get it to start again, let alone
get it anywhere near its old condition."

"Well you try," I said, like I was

getting mad, "but I say it's a piece of junk."

Then I walked out before he could realize I knew he'd strung together more than six words at once.

After that I thought he'd freeze himself to death working on that car. He was out there all day, and at night he rigged up a little lamp, ran a cord out the window, and had himself some light to see by while he worked. He was better than he had been before, but that's still not saying much. It was easier for him to do the things the rest of us did. He ate more slowly and didn't jump up and down during the meal to get this or that or look out the window. I put my hand in the back of the TV set, I admit, and fiddled around with it good, so that it was almost impossible now to get a clear picture. He didn't look at it very often anyway. He was always out with that car or going off to get parts for it.

By the time it was really melting outside, he had it fixed.

I had been feeling down in the dumps about Henry around this time. We had always been together before. Henry and Lyman. But he was such a loner now that I didn't know how to take it. So I jumped at the chance one day when Henry seemed friendly. It's not that he smiled or anything. He just said, "Let's take that old shitbox for a spin." Just the way he said it made me think he could be coming around.

We went out to the car. It was spring. The sun was shining very bright. My only sister, Bonita, who was just eleven years old, came out and made us stand together for a picture. Henry leaned his elbow on the red car's windshield, and he took his other arm and put it over my shoulder, very carefully, as though it was heavy for him to lift and he didn't want to bring the weight down all at once.

"Smile," Bonita said, and he did.

• • • •

That picture. I never look at it any-
more. A few months ago, I don't know
why, I got his picture out and tacked it
on the wall. I felt good about Henry at
the time, close to him. I felt good hav-
ing his picture on the wall, until one
night when I was looking at television. I
was a little drunk and stoned. I looked
up at the wall and Henry was staring at
me. I don't know what it was, but his
smile had changed, or maybe it was gone.
All I know is I couldn't stay in the same
room with that picture. I was shaking. I
got up, closed the door, and went into
the kitchen. A little later my friend Ray
came over and we both went back into
that room. We put the picture in a brown
bag, folded the bag over and over tightly,
then put it way back in a closet.

I still see that picture now, as if it
tugs at me, whenever I pass that closet
door. The picture is very clear in my
mind. It was so sunny that day Henry
had to squint against the glare. Or maybe

the camera Bonita held flashed like a mirror, blinding him, before she snapped the picture. My face is right out in the sun, big and round. But he might have drawn back, because the shadows on his face are deep as holes. There are two shadows curved like little hooks around the ends of his smile, as if to frame it and try to keep it there—that one, first smile that looked like it might have hurt his face. He has his field jacket on and the worn-in clothes he'd come back in and kept wearing ever since. After Bonita took the picture, she went into the house and we got into the car. There was a full cooler in the trunk. We started off, east, toward Pembina and the Red River because Henry said he wanted to see the high water.

The trip over there was beautiful. When everything starts changing, drying up, clearing off, you feel like your whole life is starting. Henry felt it, too. The top was down and the car hummed like a top. He'd really put it back in shape, even the tape on the seats was very carefully put down and glued back in layers. It's not that he smiled again or even joked, but his face looked to me as if it was clear, more peaceful. It looked as though he wasn't thinking of anything in particular except the bare fields and windbreaks and houses we were passing.

The river was high and full of winter trash when we got there. The sun was still out, but it was colder by the river. There were still little clumps of dirty snow here and there on the banks. The water hadn't gone over the banks yet, but it would, you could tell. It was just at its limit, hard swollen, glossy like an old gray scar. We made ourselves a fire, and we sat down and watched the current go. As I watched it I felt something squeezing inside me and tightening and trying to let go all at the same time. I knew I was not just feeling it myself; I knew I was feeling what Henry was going through at that moment. Except that I couldn't stand it, the closing and opening. I jumped to my feet. I took Henry by the shoulders and I started shaking him. "Wake up," I says, "wake up, wake up, wake up!" I didn't know what had come over me. I sat down beside him again.

His face was totally white and hard. Then it broke, like stones break all of a sudden when water boils up inside them.

"I know it," he says. "I know it. I can't help it. It's no use."

We start talking. He said he knew what I'd done with the car. It was obvious it had been whacked out of shape and not just neglected. He said he wanted to give the car to me for good now, it was no use. He said he'd fixed it just to give it back and I should take it.

"No way," I says, "I don't want it."

"That's okay," he says, "you take it."

"I don't want it, though," I says back to him, and then to emphasize, just to emphasize, you understand, I touch his shoulder. He slaps my hand off.

"Take that car," he says.

"No," I say, "make me," I say, and then he grabs my jacket and rips the arm loose. That jacket is a class act, suede with tags and zippers. I push Henry backwards, off the log. He jumps up and bowls me over. We go down in a clinch and come up swinging hard, for all we're worth, with our fists. He socks my jaw so hard I feel like it swings loose. Then I'm at his ribcage and land a good one under his chin so his head snaps back. He's dazzled. He looks at me and I look at him and then his eyes are full of tears and blood and at first I think he's crying. But no, he's laughing. "Ha! Ha!" he says. "Ha! Ha! Take good care of it."

"Okay," I says, "okay, no problem. Ha! Ha!"

I can't help it, and I start laughing, too. My face feels fat and strange, and after a while I get a beer from the cooler in the trunk, and when I hand it to Henry he takes his shirt and wipes my germs off. "Hoof-and-mouth disease," he says. For some reason this cracks me up, and so we're really laughing for a while, and then we drink all the rest of the beers one by one and throw them in the river and see how far, how fast, the current takes them before they fill up and sink.

"You want to go on back?" I ask after a while. "Maybe we could snag a couple nice Kashpaw girls."

He says nothing. But I can tell his mood is turning again.

"They're all crazy, the girls up here, every damn one of them."

"You're crazy too," I say, to jolly him up. "Crazy Lamartine boys!"

He looks as though he will take this wrong at first. His face twists, then clears, and he jumps up on his feet. "That's right!" he says. "Crazier 'n hell. Crazy Indians!"

I think it's the old Henry again. He throws off his jacket and starts swinging his legs out from the knees like a fancy dancer. He's down doing something between a grouse dance and a bunny hop, no kind of dance I ever saw before, but neither has anyone else on all this green growing earth. He's wild. He wants to pitch whoopee! He's up and at me and all over. All this time I'm laughing so hard, so hard my belly is getting tied up in a knot.

"Got to cool me off!" he shouts all of a sudden. Then he runs over to the river and jumps in.

There's boards and other things in the current. It's so high. No sound comes from the river after the splash he makes, so I run right over. I look around. It's getting dark. I see he's halfway across the water already, and I know he didn't swim there but the current took him. It's far. I hear his voice, though, very clearly across it.

"My boots are filling," he says.

He says this in a normal voice, like he just noticed and he doesn't know what to think of it. Then he's gone. A branch comes by. Another branch. And I go in.

By the time I get out of the river, off the snag I pulled myself onto, the sun is down. I walk back to the car, turn on the high beams, and drive it up the bank. I put it in first gear and then I take my foot off the clutch. I get out, close the door, and watch it plow softly into the water. The headlights reach in as they go down, searching, still lighted even after the water swirls over the back end. I wait. The wires short out. It is all finally dark. And then there is only the water, the sound of it going and running and going and running and running.

Your Thoughts about the Selection
from *Love Medicine*

1. What did you think of the selection from *Love Medicine*? Did you like it? Why?

2. Are there any ways that the events or people in the selection became important or special to you? Write or discuss why.

3. What parts of the selection were the most interesting? Why?

4. Was the ending what you expected it would be? If not, what did you expect and why?

5. Was there anything new or surprising to you in the selection? What?

Thinking about the Story

1. Describe the people in the selection from *Love Medicine*. Which do you think is the most important? Why?

2. Louise Erdrich does not tell us specifically whether Henry drowned by accident or on purpose. Which do you think? Why?

3. In some fiction, *where* the story takes place is important. This story takes place on a reservation. In what ways is the place important or not important to the story?

4. As you were listening or reading, what were your thoughts as the story unfolded?

5. Were any parts of the selection difficult to understand? If so, you may want to read or listen to them again. You might think about why they were difficult.

Thinking about the Writing

1. How did Louise Erdrich help you see, hear, and feel what happened in the story? Find the words, phrases, or sentences that you think did this the best.

2. Writers think about their stories' settings, characters, and events. In writing this story, which of these things do you think Louise Erdrich felt was most important? Find the parts of the story that support your opinion.

3. Which character was most interesting to you? How did Louise Erdrich help you learn about this person? Find the places in the selection where you learned the most about this person.

4. In the selection, Louise Erdrich uses dialogue. Dialogue can make a story stronger and more alive. Pick out some dialogue that you feel is strong, and explain how it helps the story.

5. The selection is seen through Lyman Lamartine's eyes. He uses the words "I" and "me." How would the writing be different if the story was told from another character's point of view (such as Henry's), or from your own point of view?

6. In this story, Louise Erdrich creates a feeling of tension. Right from the beginning, you have a feeling that something terrible is going to happen. Go back to the story and see which parts make you feel this tension.

Activities

1. Were there any words that were difficult for you in the selection from *Love Medicine*? Go back to these words and try to figure out their meanings. Discuss what you think each word means, and why you made that guess.

2. Are there any words new to you in the selection that you would like to remember? Discuss with your teacher or another student how you are going to remember each word. You could put them on file cards, or write them in your journal, or create a personal dictionary. Be sure to use each word in a sentence of your own.

3. How did you help yourself understand the selection? Did you ask yourself questions? What were they? Discuss these questions with other people who have read the same selection, or write about them in your journal.

4. Talking with other people about what you have read can increase your understanding of it. Discussion can help you organize your thoughts, get new ideas, and rethink your original ideas. Discuss your thoughts about the selection with someone else who has read it. Find out if your opinions are the same or different. See if your thoughts change as a result of this discussion.

5. If you like the selection, you might want to encourage someone else to read it. You could write a book review, or a letter to a friend you think might be interested in reading the book.

6. Did reading the selection give you
    any ideas for your own writing?
    You might want to write about:

    • your own relationship with a
      brother or sister.
    • a person you have known who
      has a problem such as depression.
    • a special possession and what it
      meant to you.

7. If you could talk to Louise Erdrich,
    what questions would you ask
    about her writing? You might want
    to write the questions in your
    journal.

8. The Lamartine brothers are Native
    Americans. Some things about them
    are unique because of their cultural
    background. You might want to
    write about what makes you unique
    because of your own cultural
    background.

9. War makes a deep impression on those who fight and on those who wait at home. You might interview someone who has been to war or someone whose loved one served. Make a list of questions to ask them. You might write an article based on the interview.

10. Is there something you kept thinking about after reading the selection? What? Write about why it is meaningful to you.

References and Resources

Books by Louise Erdrich

Jacklight (poems), Henry Holt, 1984
Love Medicine (novel), Henry Holt, 1984
The Beet Queen (novel), Henry Holt, 1986
Tracks (novel), Henry Holt, 1988

Books About Native Americans

Dee Brown, *Bury My Heart at Wounded Knee,* Holt, 1970

Vine Deloria, Jr., *Custer Died for Your Sins,* Macmillan, 1969

Wayne Moquin with Charles van Doren, editors, *Great Documents in American History,* Praeger, 1973

Carol Waldman, *Atlas of the North American Indian,* Facts on File, 1985

Books About Vietnam

Bernard Edelman, editor, *Dear America: Letters Home from Vietnam,* Norton, 1985

Jan C. Scruggs and Joel L. Swerdlow, *To Heal a Nation,* Harper & Row, 1985

Movies About Vietnam

Apocalypse Now
Coming Home
Dear America
The Deer Hunter
Full Metal Jacket
Platoon

Writers' Voices

☐ Rudolfo A. Anaya, *Selected from* BLESS ME, ULTIMA 0–929631–06–4 $2.95

☐ Maya Angelou, *Selected from* I KNOW WHY THE CAGED BIRD SINGS *and* THE HEART OF A WOMAN 0–929631–04–8 $2.95

☐ Carol Burnett, *Selected from* ONE MORE TIME 0–929631–03–X $2.95

☐ Avery Corman, *Selected from* KRAMER VS. KRAMER 0–929631–01–3 $2.95

☐ Bill Cosby, *Selected from* FATHERHOOD *and* TIME FLIES 0–929631–00–5 $2.95

☐ Louise Erdrich, *Selected from* LOVE MEDICINE 0–929631–02–1 $2.95

New Writers' Voices

☐ SPEAKING OUT ON HEALTH, *An Anthology* 0–929631–05–6 $2.95

To order any of these books, please send your check or money order (no cash, please) to Publishing Program, Literacy Volunteers of New York City Inc., Suite 520, 666 Broadway, New York, NY 10012. Please add $1.50 per order and 50¢ per book to cover postage and handling. New York and Connecticut residents, add appropriate sales tax. If you are a tax-exempt organization, include a copy of your exemption certificate with your order. For information on bulk discounts, please contact the Sales Manager at the above address.